Me and My Mum

5

First published in 2009
by Wayland

This paperback edition published in 2010 by Wayland

Text copyright © Amanda Rainger 2009
Illustration copyright © Simone Abel 2009

Wayland
338 Euston Road
London NW1 3BH

Wayland Australia
Level 17/207 Kent Street
Sydney, NSW 2000

Series Editor: Louise John
Cover design: Paul Cherrill
Design: D.R.ink
Consultant: Shirley Bickler

A CIP catalogue record for this book is available from the British Library.

ISBN 9780750258081 (hbk)
ISBN 9780750260244 (pbk)

Printed in China

Wayland is a division of Hachette Children's Books,
an Hachette UK Company

www.hachette.co.uk

Me and My Mum

Written by Amanda Rainger
Illustrated by Simone Abel

WAYLAND

My mum is really pretty.
Her name is Mary Lou.

4

Her hair is brown and curly,
and her eyes are blue.

We live with my pet rabbit
in a funny old flat.

His fur is soft and fluffy.
He is getting very fat.

In my bedroom I keep
all my books and my toys.

I like computer games,
but Mum hates the noise.

I have dinosaur curtains,
and a dinosaur rug.

I have stars on my walls,
and a tiger to hug.

We go out in the morning
at half past eight.

We hurry to school
so I won't be late.

Mum works in a shop.
It's called Save and Spend.

She brings me home cakes
that I share with my friends.

At half past six
we wave to Nan.

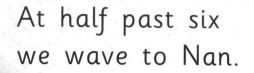

We hurry back home
as fast as we can.

Then I tell Mum
what I did at school.

I give her my picture –
she thinks it is cool.

19

Mum reads me a story
and we say, "Good night."

She gives me a kiss.
Then she puts out the light.

My Mum is really pretty.
Her name is Mary Lou.

I love my Mum,
and she loves me too!

START READING is a series of highly enjoyable books for beginner readers. **The books have been carefully graded to match the Book Bands widely used in schools.** This enables readers to be sure they choose books that match their own reading ability.

Look out for the Band colour on the book in our Start Reading logo.

The Bands are:

	Pink Band 1A & 1B
	Red Band 2
	Yellow Band 3
	Blue Band 4
	Green Band 5
	Orange Band 6
	Turquoise Band 7
	Purple Band 8
	Gold Band 9

START READING books can be read independently or shared with an adult. They promote the enjoyment of reading through satisfying stories supported by fun illustrations.

Amanda Rainger writes books and TV programmes for children learning French and Spanish. Best of all, she likes making up songs and stories – especially in rhyme! She works in a shed in the garden, with a tortoise, a fox and a chaffinch for company.

Simone Abel has illustrated over 200 books for children and has even won some awards. Best of all, she likes drawing people and animals, although she has just finished illustrating a book about cakes, which was great fun! She lives in Yorkshire, with her husband who is a painter, and their two daughters.